to Henry

Would that my words rise and
fall with the occasion.

*My most heartfelt thanks
to my dear friend Noreen Greeno
and my daughter Kelley Seaton
without whose help this book
could not have been completed*

Table
of Contents

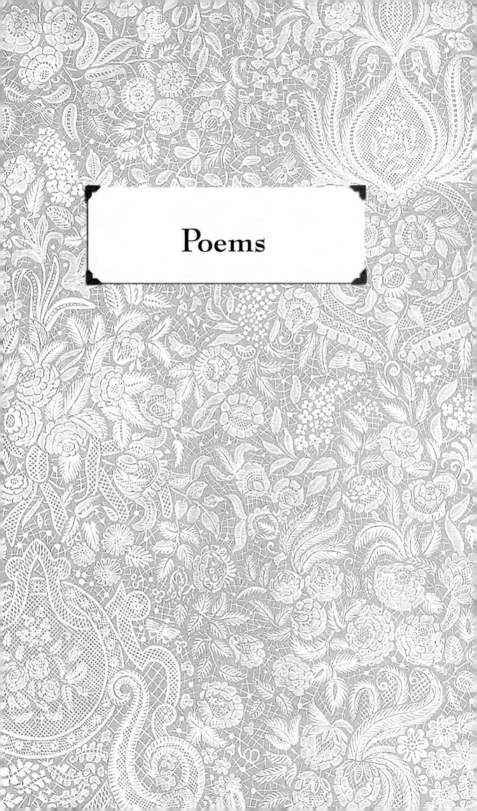

Poems

Letters Home

On a rainy day I found the letters
in a trunk long in the attic,
and a doughboy and a G.I. came alive.

Young soldiers both, beautiful, innocent.
One wounded pulling a dying comrade
into a trench in France, 1917;
the other, his son, lost at sea
in another war, 1943.

Letters home, written on thin yellowed paper,
frayed with reading and rereading,
stained with tears,
tied with faded ribbon.

The words breathed from the pages,
brave words fraught with frailties humanly fresh
by boy-heroes concealing homesick longing,
dread of battle, fear of death,
their youth impaled with a legacy
of resounding duty and honor
weaving its time into infinity,
embossing hearts now
and tomorrow and tomorrow,
telling and retelling of survival never finished.

Rain down the attic window dripped
like blood spilling
when monsters seize power
and mothers lose sons.

To Labor in a New Vineyard

Has wee legacy of words I scribble of a day
and run through the gristmill of crafting
clean lines in rhythm
ear testing voice prevail
proved I did toil
here for a season?

Or will it go down
as unworthy of the sweat of my brow,
piquing a passion for perfection?

Leaves fall into the vast silence
of winter;
blood thickens and time stills
the season fading
nevermore visited nor altered.

All the earth bows
as the page turns
to a clean start and another chance
to labor in the vineyard
of a new season.

In My Own Backyard

if happiness be found
I must hurry track it down
one road then another
I chase
errant paths wending
through forests rivers hills
I wander in a desert
grasping for pleasures

nearly home
I pause by the roadside
with a fellow traveler
we sample fruit
smell the rain
chat over cold lemonade

together we plant a fallow field
water
share a harvest
give thanks
happiness our reward
again and again

Keep Your Foot
in the Door

I'm rounding the curve and options
are dropping off.
"Too late," readily comes to mind.

Some day I would
conduct a symphony,
dye my hair red,
earn a law degree,
live in a Victorian mansion.
"Some days" are running out.

Should I inventory
past performances
they would fill volumes, I suppose.
Could I now train myself
to idle time
would peace prevail?
Complacency seems
an early form of death;
as long as life pulses
the drive is forward,
conquer,
keep your foot in the door.

Surely passionate accuracy
and depth of perception follow
the duty to record our times;
when life's action
is so distant in the past
I cannot bring it up fresh and vivid.

When the last door closes
God grant me the grace fearless
to record my last thought.

Farm Fresh

Morning rays stream through
Mist in the meadow
Colts awaken, darting and charging
A rooster crows
His hens pick and cluck
Through the barnyard

August flies buzz bean-snapping laps
Breezes through screen windows
Stir Dutch lace curtains

Pie apples and fresh eggs
Rest on the dry sink
While bacon fries and toast browns
Windsor chairs are pulled up
To the table set with a clean blue cloth

Pyre on the Mountain

On a large day in a land apart
surreal purple hills wrapped
in delicate pastel brush strokes
rise beyond fragile valleys;

mountains, brittle and parched with drought,
quiver as crimson flames lick the sky;
deer flee high ground through black smoke;
river dwellers escape
with the clothes on their backs;

tomorrow's stark pinons and aspens
already stand like charred sentinels
to the ashes on the mountainside,
their creek beds too dry for tears.

October All Over

Late in the year, late in life,
papers in order—well, almost;
a few doors close again this year,
no more starting new tasks.

But who now should hurry along?
When the job is done will be soon enough;
we'll do what we can while we can
and let the rest fall where it will.

Retired, though tired is a bit more apt,
our road is still open and our lights are on.
The RV in the drive suggests we still travel
south for the winter, north for the summer.

Our children are each one a joy,
the grandchildren free miles plus bonus;
and if we are still having birthdays,
light the candles and save me the waltz.

Would He Trade Me Places?

Mr. Pigeon lights on my balcony
and waddles into my room
ogling and picking
then out again, he flies away
does he soar in ecstasy
or has he fear of heights
does he surf the waves with no thought
of tomorrow
or today
does a cloud mean peril
or a drink of water and a bath
is he of the ruling class
or an underling
does he have a day's agenda
deadlines
property taxes
health insurance
a retirement plan

would he trade me places?
would I?

Seniors' Day
at the Races

visor caps and hair dye cover heads
bald, white, blond or red
faces pinched and dried
cigarette smoke trailing off
yellow fingers

faded eyes staring out
at the dusty track

too stiff to rise
the seniors sit barely aware
of eight greyhounds pumping
their hearts out
to place on a racing form
they can't read

Hurry Up and Weight

'Til now each season went by like another.
The challenge was climbing a slippery ladder,
a briefcase heavy with hard-earned weight
of slaving all hours, don't dare be late,
scaling the ranks at backbreaking pace
for fear of losing your place in the race
to beat a clock you'd sooner ignore
in the struggle to top an elusive score.

At last sweet retirement; golden years follow,
though many who've been there say "carefree" rings hollow.
Hip joints and transplants might borrow some time
while you wait in the wings for the show to resign.
But hear what I say, and listen up good:
don't fool mother nature's volatile mood.
Gravity's pull is her class-act betrayal
'cause face lifts destroy the control of your spittle!

Goodbye Santa Fe

your name enchanting
your barrios, your hills
of age-old adobe enclaves pre-dated
scientific debacles
a walk through your streets
and time stood still
untouchable
incorruptible

not so long ago
white man sneaked in with thoughts
of profit
I was one
we would procure your handwork
market it
make you rich
for a price

goodbye Santa Fe
you perish on the poison
parasites fed you
flattery hoodwinked you beneath
superstructures of movie star proportions
whose price-tag pretense

lured your rich traditions
into greedy hands
you traded communal security
for competitive poverty

goodbye Santa Fe
your tardy chieftains now rise up
to oust us charlatans
and reclaim your past

goodbye Santa Fe
you sold out to the good times
too late you want it back for free
goodbye simple hearts
I remember your sweetness

Winter, Your Nickel has Run Out

Loose me from your wooden arms, house;
your ceaseless winter monologue drums
through rooms wrapped in tourniquets
of worsted wool and blood-red velvet.

Cut to Act 3, closing scene.
Kill the footlights,
bring down the curtain,
clear the stage;
write a fresh script
smelling sea-clean,
sailing on crisp backdrops.

Re-open to summer sets
of wicker and chintz,
stirring Sousa in the park,
bicycles built for two.

Set off the sky
in red white and blue
with franchised freedom flashing! flashing!
like the Fourth of July!

The Apology

just when safe landing seemed possible
the elusive shore clouds again
and a deluge of cold water swamps
my tiny craft

asea again, storms on all sides threaten
hopes for a rainbow
it came today midway
crushing rocks on the chest
embroiling outrage like waves of nausea

what happened to innocent until proven guilty
not in this life
can't have benefit of doubt
the Peter Principle drives in reverse
get him before he does something good

where is the opiate to dispel
this pulsing blood red rib routing force
has God taken a hike

but wait

deliverance: an apology!

in one instant I am dragged
from the canyon of despair
to the epiphany of the mountain top

Driftwood

he turns to look at her
straight nose wide eyes
familiar once now a stranger
a warm ally turned hostile
when

why

their union asea drifts off-course

they sit at a table
lie in the same bed
the gap widening

try the more
the bridge ends mid-air

Winter Tantrum

wench wind whips
a froth of ice-wash onslaught
storming in legions
a hundredfold abreast
snapping saplings
limbs and lines
with impartial wrath

taking no prisoners

avenging what scorn

Reel Going 'Round and 'Round

they're coming
they're coming tonight
coming to dinner
coming with hurts
hurts too new
too old

in the dark she's tried to sort them out

how

why

he lives somewhere in the back of his head
a wanton compulsion for straying
plays like a home movie
defeating the better judgment
of an old fool

she cannot access the dark brooding
face anchored in stone creases
nor his center
born and formed
in mean-spirit/small-mind/small-town/hometown

she has not in the passage of their marriage
pried him open even a crack
too many years spent
too few left for a new start

we sit carefully at table
they hardly try now
the reels play and replay
she chips away
out of halfhearted habit
the chips lie on the table

Burden of Sentry

she watched for the moment
careful to seize and choke it off
no new days; they are planned
long in advance
to her satisfaction
her delight
in fashioning his constraints
free movement not his
the dogs have free movement

a bitter cup of tea steeps
hate seeking a cause
hate her final good deed

he ignores her chipping
knowing she'll have her way
she conducts him with baton
thwarting his wishes
guarding his friendships

tall
handsome
she displays him on a flagpole
then shoots him down for all to see

he lives in captivity
she is keeper of the door

control slowly strangling each

Cruel Hope

At a dark night hour meant for sleep
I sit tasting great salt tears,
stick legs cradled in my arms.

Harbored visions
of returning power sustained
the morning, morning, and morning;

a thunderbolt of truth
long postponed
drains my wellspring hope,
mornings have run out,
goodbye, my legs my legs,
I remember the way we were.

Will the Crop Harvest?

We're at marriage crossroads again;
for the hundredth time fresh air for you
is no air for me.

In the early blush of youth
unending commitment sounded romantic,
compromise harmless;
our wills ever sliced in pieces
never occurred to us.
You were my rogue
and I your toy doll;
we ran like a pack
and never lifted our heads.

Fragile and brittle, you found hiding places;
I forever looked to flush you out.
We crawled along surfaces
and split and branched,
our roots tangled and couldn't separate;
our bitter crop
of gold and glitter and eternal youth
had no harvest;
we were dying in our desert.

We dug ourselves up,
transplanting ourselves in primitive northern soil,
turning in slow forgiving seasons.
Winter serenity enfolds old wounds,
summer waves sweep away scars
like etchings in the sand.

Our roots are taking hold, deepening;
perhaps in time we'll earn
a sunny spot in the garden.

Polonaise in A-flat

Compelling waves of power
state the purposeful authority
of the first movement,
its impact held in check.

Shifting suddenly,
the whimsical searching patterns
of the middle movement
wind in and out
through uncertain mazes,
building momentum,
preparing to
rejoin the original theme restated
in a final thrust.

Victorious ending chords
resound off the rafters!

Carry Me Back

they say I'm crazy now
rolling in ruts
and circles
trained on escape
searching
for Greeks and Victorians
their porches spread for sitting
and sipping mint juleps and listening
to ghostly holdovers
correct and formal
speaking with eloquent tongues of the masters
literature
sea voyages
that floated away somewhere
faintly in the distance
driven off by rap and rock and graffiti

carry me back on a fine trolley car
fragrant with cherries in bloom
to a love
handsome and tall
chivalrous
who tips his hat and bows
and finds me pleasing

Pursuit or Destination

if happiness be destination
what road must I travel
I try one path, then another
chasing a forever fleeting feast
misadventure and other errant trails wend
through forests, over rivers, up hills
I wander in a desert, confused
by promising pleasures perceived as permanent
in my quest I fail to find
so busy am I seeking

if, on the other hand, happiness be the pursuit
would I so hasten to forge on
rather would I pass slowly, sampling
sweet fruits, taking time
to chat with a friend
over cold lemonade
strolling together through a fragrant rose garden
of yellow, pink, and red

would I till a fallow field, plant, water
share a harvest, give thanks

pursuit circles each year
again and again

destination is so . . . final

Keep Me To You

If I go today without intention
leaving little upon which to lean
save few memories of deeds cut short
these long years,
forgive me for the times I've been too heavy
when endurance bankrupted health.

Believe I would my misplaced wellness in this life
be added to yours hence
and never run out.

Do not grieve my absence,
for I will meet you
in surprising places
and bear with you your worst and best.

Wear me then as regal garment
entitling honor;
keep me to you as a richer portion;
remember me as you would I be
and forgive yourself
as you would me.

Don't let me die for lack,
nor stray from memory marked in marrow,
borne in blood, held in heart,

for I live on in such places
as make room.

Grace Full of Grace

She shone more radiant than most
Arresting awe
Her core fresh as apple.
A sharp mind and spirit dwelt
In frail flesh dulled
Not one bit with age (and sometimes
neither her tongue.)

Everyone's mother, she mothered
No one; gave full grown
Stature even to children.

Hers a heart honed to patience,
Softened with humility,
Epitomized in peace.

Grace, aptly named, believed
To the last we were the generous ones;
Enthroned as head mistress
From whom we drew beyond
Our share, now poses
The very hardest lesson: learning how
To go on without her.

I see her yet with her yellow-green bag
Carrying her worldly goods,
Blowing kisses lovely as lilac
And gently traveling on.

To Tasha

She came to us a wavy ball
of shiny black red tongue
ready with kisses
eyes trusting
tail wagging

She learned the English language
and how to spell it
she opened doors
waited in the tub for a bath
she mothered the kittens
pulled a child from the lake
rode in the passenger seat
ate her own ice cream sundae

She grew to lustrous Newfoundland stature
her paws resting on our shoulders
she ruled our hearts
taught us to forgive
to love for no reason
to carry no grudge

Her time came suddenly today
without warning
we held her
said our good-byes
let her go

We cherish her collar
a lock of hair
her squeeze toy
a photo

Two Lives Join

In quiet partnership
committed,
strengthened one to the other
by loyalty and faith,
may the union you've courage to enter
endure.
May the fortitude to forgive
those who would persecute
never fail you.
May you find solace
within your loving hearts
and may timeless peace bless
your best efforts.
May the boundless love and devotion
held in my heart
protect and keep you always.

Tides Abate

Billy, my son of peace,
whom peace eludes
the more deserving
gentle heart woven special
to mine since birth
your toil diligent and ceaseless
well marked with pride
by all
and in the final hour
pandemonium rears
sapping Eden

have no guilt have no fear
you shall overcome

hearts here pump with yours
empowering great courage
our love prolific
if we ride tides of hardship
yet awhile
be strong my son
take heart

your family with Christ is
before you
behind you
beside you
above you
beneath you
within you

The Battle Won,
Here Comes the War

Ten years measures the toil
of student muscles pouring
the foundation amassing credentials
flood nor famine dare claim.

Shift gears
enter phase two
a workaday world
where permanence and community reside
expectations ride high
and overshoot the runway
the checkbook high
among the casualty count.

(Keep those guitars strumming.)

For while the cars die
Tom breaks through the deck
the iguana eats the cat
the grass keeps right on growing.

Face it! This is as good as it gets.

All in One Beloved

She's the sun glinting off purple waves
The glee in a carameled apple
The spice of sweet and sour

She's fresh wit
Biting as jalapeno

She's a lollipop of five
A rose of thirty
A sage of ninety

Her flavors seep through and blend
In a rich liqueur
Somber on tongue
Brandy warm going down

Jump-Start Your Life

you have climbed your slope
and the world lies waiting
paths traveled and untraveled
lead up mountains
and wind through valleys

see the large picture
keep your ambition in sight
through short-term whims
and side adventures

knowledge and appetite for service
feed the heart and temper the spirit
their pursuit infuses the flow
of your natural gifts
a hundredfold

dare to greet each day
expecting the best
taking what comes in kind
leaving behind sensibilities
and other baggage

your carriage and demeanor
reflect a rare star quality
be attuned to your magic
believe in a world
responsive to your radiance
eager to enfold
your magnificent heart

Portrait of an Unsung Hero

I should look to the masters'
eloquent rhymes to tell
you what is in my heart
with my own crude words
I can only try:

you are my love, my courage,
my reason, my strength,
my joy, my legs,
my foundation, my ambition,

you travel the depths
the heights, the longest mile,
the distance, and never lose
heart, my greatest hero.

You deserve all rewards
they are too many and not enough;
my words, too, fall short,
they're all I have;
I give them to you now
along with my life.

A Day in the Life of Rae Ann

And what mystique lies behind
This breathtaking child,
A Mona Lisa
Who keeps herself secret?

She moves through a garden
Picking and choosing,
Gathering tiny blossoms,
Chasing butterflies,
Splashing in the birdbath.

She shakes Grandma's Rolaids can
Like a rhythmic castanet,
Giving the raccoon brothers chase.

She runs for Grandma's lap,
Grabs the wheelchair throttle
Squealing over the cat's tail.

The piano is next; her favorite!
She hammers away,
Searching for the rhapsody she knows
To be in there somewhere!

It's dinner time and the Sandman approaches
Eyelids grow heavy.
Mona Lisa smiles
and blows a nigh' nigh' kiss.

We lay her down to sleep
And pray the Lord her soul to keep.

Tom, Tom, Gentle of Heart

Just last week you gathered butterflies
and caterpillars, lizards, toads and turtles.

Only yesterday a giant wake
foamed onto our shore;
it was you out there, Tom, at the helm
(hardly able to see over the steering wheel
last I remember.)
Now you say you're graduating from high school,
poised to branch out
on your own limb?

The Riviera, the fjords, ski slopes, air balloons,
frescos, Eiffel Towers beckon? And oh, yes,
pretty girls to chase you?

May the Lord's blessings go with you
and the wind be always at your back.

Happenstance far out on your limb
the world should tip and deceive,
bloody your nose, black your eyes,
listen to these lips:
stand your ground, Grandson;
reclaim the power of your roots
and ever dare to be who you are!

Twenty-Five Years Measure

The romantic overture
Began in a sunny garden
Embraced by best friends
Family and ice sculptures
All beneath a backdrop of love.

As high expectations quivered
Young moods wore thin
Solid rock ground
Into shifting sand
Against a backdrop of love.

Toughing it out and surviving
Bought the gifts of grace and gratitude
Today and tomorrow
Against the same everlasting
Backdrop of love
Which laid the groundwork of eloquence
As your brilliant fledglings
Of song add their wealth
To the mix.

Hearts swell
As the handprints
Of your loving efforts manifest.
Boundaries expand
And you rise and perfect and increase.
You've performed the twenty five year
Overture
Success increasing
Like the worth of silver.

Around the Corner

White snow blew
down the street yesterday,
past the house all dark now,
all in it gone,
disappeared around another corner.
No flowers spilling down the banks this year.

Do your flowers grow around the corner
and take up where they left off?
Is there spring in steps so far away
picking up the beat dropped but shortly?

We try to patch the hole time left,
imagining we watch the same Seinfeld,
meet at Perkins,
keep Shabbat,
touch for a moment.

Time advances and parting scars will heal,
but not today.
Today pain reels too far across the heart,
swallowing the sun.

From this Day Forward

a vision in white moves forward
on Bachstrings in G
veiled perfection
of the child-woman stuns
the satin train passes
dearest memories surging
without mercy
love-tears drop
on the arm
bearing her

who gives this bride
treasure her we beg
with this ring
as we once did
till death do part
as we will hence

Jesu, joy of man, keep
her from this day

Goodbye My Flower

yet a bud with full-bloom promise
though blood drips at the parting
our wordless bond remains
wear your magic cloak and trust its powers
to move you on with faith
in parents and grandparents
my bud with full-bloom promise

honor our good we pray
and forgive each abrasion seventy times seven
would that the world be gentle and generous with you
that your fragrance pleases as your violin
that your eager sprouts prevail
through best and bleakest days
my bud with full-bloom promise

for it is with intrepid love
we ever pick ourselves up
and go forward one more time

One Day at a Time

with hope for a family all but lost
word came of a child far over the tundra
while the tiny seed shone like a bright new penny
the baby girl blessed with beauty and wonder
the day God placed her deep in their hearts
a flower perfecting one day at a time

they named the babe Anna Belle
passed down from Anna Engler, 1852
and Anna Senn, 1923
who kept the good name
shameless and true
another Anna on the family tree
stands notably apt proud parents agree

she's made marriage a family
a joy to behold
she drives her own car
already at three
she's a priceless original
God, please keep her safe

Soaring the Skies

a whimsical rock on stormy shores
or calm at your behest
you charm as Aladdin
blazing wit ready
or dictated as Caesar
fierce and unafraid of boulders
bridling at restraints
temporary to indigenous earth
you warm the breasts of home
wandering in and about without ties
to mortal duties

the grace for kindness

fetters foreign to your field
fragile and brittle to boxes and barriers

some would say you came from Venus
not to break trails
but to travel the passive long way

a free spirit on the threshold
of the skies you so love

A Love Note

A birthday love note
scrawled on a card
lies too wilted
to hold all you are;
my pen won't aptly
write out the sonnet
held captive and silent
here in my heart.
I love you, my hero,
for all reasons and none;
I wish you your dreams,
your hopes and beyond.

Looking Both Ways

The time now one score together;
we traveled far along paths
chosen and unchosen,
blind and sighted.

I have no regrets.

Elusive Eden comes and goes
redefining itself at will.

I have no illusions.

Moss truly gathered
shimmers with tears and struggle;
sacrifice and devotion weld
our hard-earned marriage.

I'd have no other.

With honor and integrity
charting the way,
no matter the destination.

I have no doubts.

Our love is power and courage
to taste tomorrow's fare.

I have no fear.

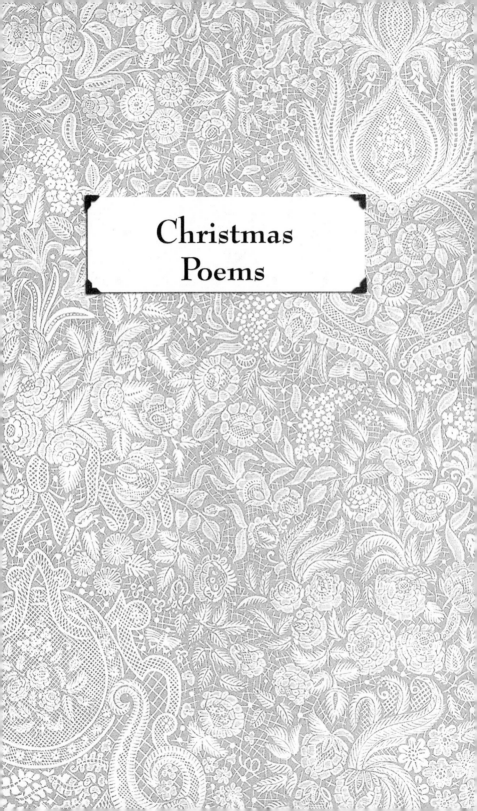

Christmas
Poems

May Peace Reign Sweetly

your sun smiles at us over the horizon
warming our empty nest
drawing us close
blessing us with family

may your good heart lead you
where you keep your dreams
and good fortune follow
without question
through caramels and callouses
bitter and sweet
passing all understanding
enduring for all time

Christmas 2000

in the deep winter forest
deer foraging
pause
oaks and maples
naked and childless
stand alert
one bright star
shows the way
promising
PEACE
among all men of good will

Christmas Poem

a
north
wind sends
December
powderflakes
spiraling in white
scrolls across winter
flats

my barren slate impaled
with burden awaits
quivering for word
heralding hope
trumpeting joy
promising

Peace

The Christchild Promised

The sun shines through my glass roof
warming the early morning chill,
burning off the layers of sleep
yet infested with yesterday's fears
wherein harsh reprisals are born.
May the Christchild promised this day
soften the sharp edges of my heart
and restore a deep abiding peace.

Waters Run Silent

Deer forage in the meadow,
nibbling dauntless evergreens,
robbing bird feeders.
Oaks and maples, bare
and childless, await
a primitive creche to fashion.

Waters run silent 'neath the ice;
and written in white swirls atop,
God's promise of
Hope and Peace
to all men of good will.

Polar Bear Pines

Winter swirls 'round string lights
Wrapped in snow-laden polar bear pines
Claw branches wave joy
To the world
Angels hark
Heaven and nature sing
Of Peace

Peace Wavers

my lost spirit languishes
hope for good will
between nations wears thin
faith in peace among men wavers
my shriveled heart needs
another Christmas
breathing the innocent breath
of the babe wrapped
in swaddling clothes
asleep in a manger

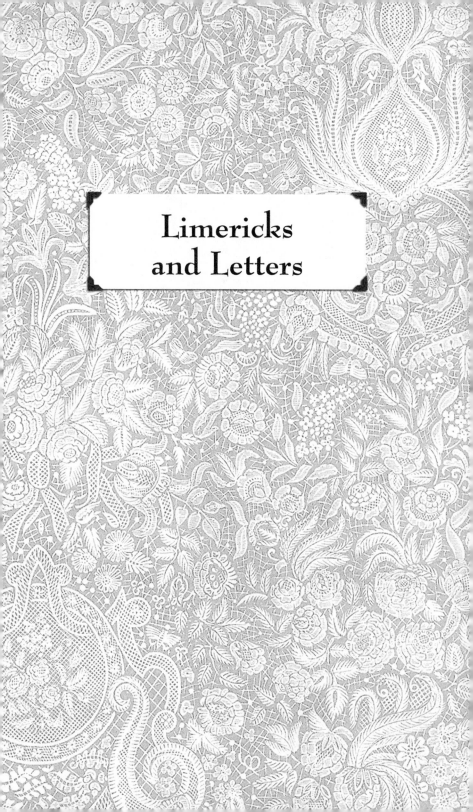

Limericks
and Letters

Limericks

On a fine August day fifty years ago,
young Bob called up Pearl on his radio.
"You wanna get hitched?"
She thought he said rich
and replied, "Won't I need a portfolio?"

———————

On a day of joint celebration,
they're bit by a square-dance fixation.
They whirl through the night
'til Helen falls, white,
leaving Harold the waltz hesitation.

———————

On a clear churning summer day whitecap,
your wintery bones in the wind flap;
bobbing like cork,
you desist and retort,
you're young yet and crisp as a winesap.

———————

Your syntax rings wide and verbosely,
sequentially spaced much too closely,
with nary a reason
why December season
should fabricate truth less purposely.

Let's for Texas Head

A hard year 'mid hard years fistfights us,
we sag beneath dread Arthur-it-is
who has a plan
for get off our can,
a jump-starter-pusher impetus.

Ammonia we need to revive us,
get up our duff off immedious.
Will twenty-weight fix
what u-joint constricts?
I've heard oil they have down in Texas.

Clifford, the Last of the Whippersnappers

At eighty-five yet a young whippersnapper,
wiry, trim and still dapper;
you dance 'til dawn
with nary a yawn,
spurning a midday cat-napper.

You scour Montana for game;
in Alaska it's salmon you claim.
Though manners are mild,
you're king of the wild,
wall trophies proving your fame.

It's known you've amassed quite a wad;
they say you've more money than God!
With cards up your sleeve,
I saw your reprieve;
if that is your secret, please nod.

We look for a long life before you,
each year a mandate for health anew;
we want you around,
you're so fun to hound,
you eighty-five year young whippersnapper, you!

Cops and Ghouls

Brainerd Daily Dispatch
506 James
Brainerd, MN 56401

Dear Editor:

Thursday a week or thereabouts, I witnessed a memorable debacle in downtown Brainerd, outside the onerous Eclectic Cafe. A dozen uniformed cops (but for budget cuts would've been two dozen, badly needed), eyes bulging, veins prominent, swarmed about, tripping over each other, jamming citations in the faces of insecure young vulnerables dressed rather like ghouls.

Suddenly, unnoticed by the martial display a few feet distant, a wino stumbled from an iniquitous watering hole nearby, teetered to his knees, belched forth, and crawling to his vehicle, climbed in, fished for keys, and after a couple of false starts careened down the public street, barely missing a senior on crutches aided across the street by one such ghoul. But enough.

Back at the infamous Eclectic, (which serves a great sandwich and exotic coffee, by the way,) our streets are safe at last.
Let's have a drum roll, please! for the twelve little rookies, armed and dangerous!

> Very truly yours,
> Vivian Senn Liners

Minto's Sara Silas

Sara Silas was the Health Aide in Minto, Alaska at the time Ms. Liners was asked by a reporter to write this letter about her for a magazine article.

Dear Ms. Ginger Place,

What a pleasant surprise today to hear you are doing an article about Sarah Silas!

She is an absolutely wonderful woman with whom I've kept in contact for some twenty-five years. I believe to this day that her lovely, quiet healing ways held all six of us who were injured in Minto on March 30th, 1978. Six of us from the village of Beetles Field were en route to Nenana in support of our school teacher against whom some charges had been made. The plane we flew in lost its engine near the Minto flats. The air strip there was near, but strong winds shortened the plane's gliding capability. The right wing of the plane struck a tree top and spun us into the ground. Lucky for us, two village men out cutting wood saw us come down and came to our rescue. They chopped us out of the wreckage, loaded us onto the back of their truck and took us to Sarah's home. She administered to us to the extent of her supplies, praying with us, making us as comfortable as possible on tables, on the floor, with makeshift pillows and warm blankets.

Most of us were in and out of consciousness, and not aware of the minutes and hours passing before a helicopter from an Airforce base outside Fairbanks finally arrived to load us and fly us to Fairbanks Memorial Hospital. The time was said to be five hours under Sarah's excellent care before help arrived. All of us passengers were hurt badly, three of us critically. We had broken ribs and other broken bones, internal injuries, concussions, a spinal cord injury. Sarah and her husband dealt with it all.

The six of us were hospitalized, some longer than others. As for me, I was in Fairbanks hospital for two months during which time Sarah and other residents of Minto came to visit us. Later I was flown to Santa Clara Valley Medical Center in California for two months of rehabilitation.

We returned to Alaska, then winter set in. In the spring my husband and I and two of our children returned to California for an easier climate for a wheelchair. I had broken my back and was paralyzed from the waist down.

I will remember always the sweet face of Sarah and her prayers. I like to send a box of Christmas goodies each year, and feel I'm together with the Minto people who are so lovely and special. One year a beautiful Christmas card came from Minto. Inside, the Minto village people had all signed it! I keep it nearby and give thanks!

I've tried to give an accounting of my experience of Sarah. I hope I told enough, hope I haven't told too much. Some details have faded from my memory over the years, but the face of Sarah is as vivid as though she were here yesterday.

Any questions, be free to call. I look forward so very much to seeing your publication and the story about Sarah.

Very truly yours,
Vivian Senn Liners

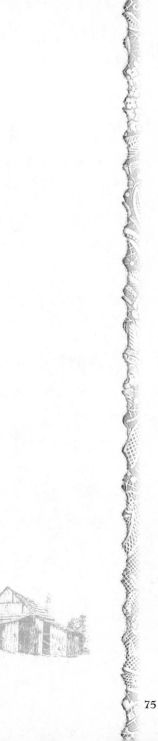

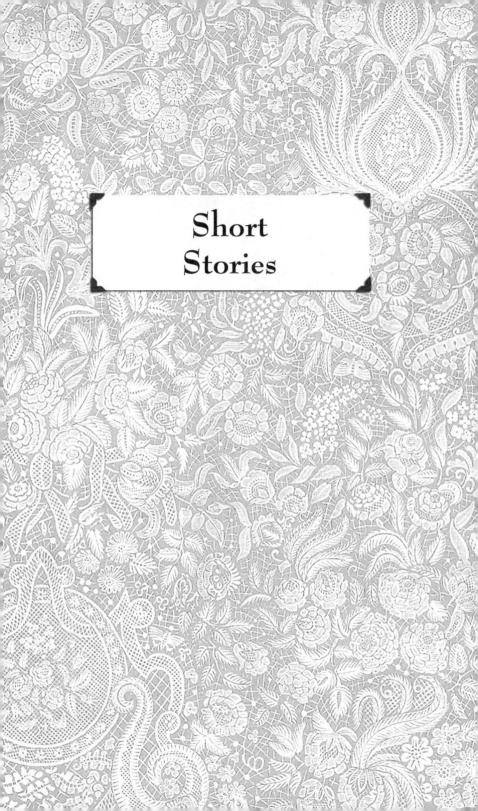

Short
Stories

No Room at the Inn

It's 10:00 p.m. We're crammed into our minivan and driving through Nevada, looking for an accessible motel room since seven o'clock. We finally give up our scenic route and wend our way toward a freeway, hoping the larger chain motels will accommodate a wheelchair.

We're tired and frustrated and rash. "You know, what we need is our own motor home." And so it is traveling began in earnest. Our 35-foot Winnebago Adventurer, loaded with every need and convenience including an electric piano, takes us first to Dothan, Alabama, where we look up friends we knew in the military whom we hadn't seen for fifty-one years. None of us has changed, right? Riding together, we spend three glorious days with them in Fairy Tale Disney World.

At last, making future plans to do it again, we tear ourselves away, and head west to do New Orleans and the French Quarter. Arriving one day after Mardi Gras, throngs of people still make merry in the streets. Everyone becomes best buddies after dark and all through the night, dancing four or five together, to great Dixieland Jazz and Cajun.

Then on to Santa Fe, where hand-crafted silver and turquoise jewelry, hand-loomed rugs, hand-thrown pottery, hand-tooled leather all speak to a primitive cell or two still lodged somewhere within each of us.

In Palm Springs we pass Bob Hope's digs sprawling over a large mesa in the Mojave desert. From our campground that evening we watch the deep red-orange-purple sunset spreading across the horizon, resounding in the chest like a Brahms overture.

Next we drive to Salinas where we park in the Elks' Club lot for ten dollars a night. For that price we can tolerate the wind and gravel blowing. We even entertain friends, serving a complete dinner on a card table with folding chairs.

In Pacific Grove we tour the giant aquarium with sea life of every size and shape and species, designed and painted by the Master Artist himself.

On to Monterey and a performance by the Monterey Symphony with guest pianist, Alexander Anissimov. Hosting a reception for musicians and family following, we again serve dinner on paperware and card tables and drink wine by candlelight.

We spend days taking in 17-Mile Drive, ogling historic mansions set on the grandest of the Pacific shores. We could not but stop in Carmel to shop. At Big Sur we watch seals and sandpipers sunning on the rocks, the aquamarine sea crashing on the beach below. Would that we somehow could capture the beauty and carry it home with us.

Then north to Auburn for breakfast with favorite friends, both in their nineties now. To avail a said shortcut, we inadvertently wind through the Sierra and its mountain switchbacks, throwing in some fervent prayers just in case. We don't recommend switchbacks to motorhomers.

But the fun is not over. Back in Minneapolis the fabulous bluegrass band, Ivory Bridge, squeezes five musicians and their instruments into our "motor hall" for some genuine foot-stomping tunes, attracting fans and curious onlookers gathered about. We are home and it is good.

Home Fires Burn Deep

As my mind roams over the cartography of our lives, the memory of one pivotal event repeatedly and persistently surfaces. At the time, I was not aware the experience would impact the family as it did. Today however, shoulda-woulda-coulda remorse leaps, accurately or not, to a turning point, and the ensuing bumps and chuckholes that jarred the routes we took.

My husband, Hal, and I began our family in a solid, traditional suburb of Minneapolis, our two-story white stucco French Colonial home high on a grassy bank. We were comfortable.

The neighborhood suited our conservative natures. By 1964 we had three school-age sons whose mischief was shared daily with the more than twenty children who lived on our block. Fall school term had already begun at St. Margaret Mary's when Hal was offered a position with a company in a small town one hundred thirty miles to the north. The prospect of relocating was incom-prehensible to me. Leaving Kullberg Studios and my twenty-four piano students, the church choir I directed, the Children's Theatre of Forest School for whom I directed and choreographed, seemed a betrayal at best. Establishing a new life in a new community, who would I then be?

Incapable of rational thought, I asked Hal to weigh the balance. He decided we would make the move.

I engaged as best I could in the industry of sorting, packing, keeping, throwing, disassembling. I plowed through the arduous ordeal with blinders, certain the children would be thrilled to live in a small town where cousins and grandparents were a daily event. I neglected to assess the effect on three young boys uprooted from everything familiar to them: play areas, trees they climbed, stores within walking distance, the rooms they'd grown in, neighborhood friends like brothers since babyhood, our block the only home they'd known. I will not forget closing and locking the door for the last time and walking down the bank

to the car and U-haul waiting. I started to turn for one last look.
Everything in me wanted one last look. "I dare not look back,"
I thought I couldn't breathe for the weight on my chest.
I climbed into the car, eyes straight ahead. As we drove off
I felt my roots tear and fall off a cliff. The scene is as vivid today.

Nor were we prepared for the misadventures that followed.
Housing was not plentiful. We moved into a four-story vintage
townhouse. A firetrap if you will. Drafts through cracks
rendered heating impossible. James, then seven, usually steady
and deliberate, carried increasing worry home from his new
school. One morning he refused to get dressed, announcing
he would not be attending "that school one more day." Two plus
two no longer totaled four. Everything was different in the new
school and he was having none of it. His teacher "was old and
crabby and should retire." Meetings with the principal brought
a spurious solution: James would be sent to a school across town
and a young teacher would deal with him. Owen, in sixth grade,
smiling and eager to charm, was nonetheless forced to tolerate
the usual taunting kids reserve for the chubby, size an advantage
only on the wrestling mats. Thirteen-year-old Edward, consummate lover of peace, met his challenge on the school steps the
first day. To his credit he replied, "No, I don't care to fight, are
you crazy?" It was only later that Edward defeated the boy badly
three times in a school-sponsored wrestling match.

I tried not to fret about the wisdom of our move. Months of
work on performance were eroding, and it wasn't long before
I fell into a bout of depression. I was in and out of hospitals with
no improvement. Grandmothers pitched in to help care for the
boys, a handful for which neither grandmas nor grandsons were
prepared. Then as though to make or break us, I found we were
to have another child. More than I could manage?

Too old at thirty-seven?

Hal was beside himself. Nervous and fatigued, he gained
weight. Disagreements within his company strained working
relationships. On one especially difficult day we sat down at the

kitchen table with a map of California, picked out a spot, and in the wake of a record January snowstorm, packed ourselves up again. The family, now including two-and-a-half-month old Mary Ellen, set out for a place in the sun.

California was wonderful with its palm trees and ocean breezes. We loved it. So did every hippy worth his salt. Spurning authority and reinventing immorality was far out, man! And though drugs ravaged him like pestilence, he still knew a good park bench when he saw it. Hal, novice owner of a fast-food restaurant, tried to acclimate to the flamboyance, often trading hamburgers for beaded necklaces and macrame. One day, putting all we had on the line, he went into hock for a camper manufacturing plant. Again our finances faltered, and so did our marriage. Badly shaken, we sold everything and paid off what we could.

Eking from the trash heap a down-payment on a small cargo plane, we set out for the frontier climate of Alaska, where Hal was about to fulfill a boyhood dream of being a bush pilot. Dream quickly turned nightmare when his first assignment took him to a bush runway near the spot where a plane in no-visibility weather crashed into a mountainside. His job: to chop nine bodies from the wreckage, put them in body-bags and fly them to Fairbanks. Every flight a risk, he eventually wrecked his plane beyond repair, miraculously without injury to himself. The final blow came thirty days later. Cajoled into a flight to the arctic to attend a meeting on behalf of the local school, I went down with five others in a Cessna 206 plane. The crash left me a paraplegic.

If only.

And so it is I drift back to 1964 and our family home and my feelings that had we never left its security, nothing bad would ever have happened to us.

Owen, now trim and handsome, returned to Minneapolis in 1996. He occasionally takes the long way home from work just to drive through the old neighborhood, past the home he remembers and always loved best. Recently he saw that it was for sale. He went to the door and knocked. When he told the owner who he was, she was kind and showed him all through the house, awakening fresh memories of his childhood Camelot. Edward, who lives in California, still avers his roots are on Zenith Avenue. He recently attended a reunion of the boys his age who'd lived on our block. Even though scattered now, not one of the boys missed the opportunity to fill in the gaps. Edward and another boy with whom he and Owen "jammed" had all three become professional musicians. Another, a skier, rose to be an Olympic ski-jumper, another an attorney. Perhaps it was something in the Zenith water. James, who stayed and worked the glitz and glamour of a Brooks' Range gold mine, left Alaska in 1982 and returned to Minnesota. Of his earliest years he remembers most fondly the red concrete road on which he trudged to school each day. It most surely gave him an appetite for colorful roads, judging from the assortment he's since walked. He likes Bemidji, where he's still picking and choosing his way through the University. Mary Ellen became from the start our salvation, the stabilizer who ordered our priorities, our surrogate home wherever we went. Since college in New York, she's returned to our state and made friends with Minneapolis, though she quips it's but a stop-off to real places.

Hal is deeply entrenched in our present home on Whitefish Lake, cherishing the proximity to our Minnesota children. Yet often when we are in the area, or sometimes even if we're not near, Hal swings by Zenith Avenue as though it were his fountain of youth. We stop and gaze, remembering Banes toddling up the steps, teeth knocked out by some tomfoolery. Or Denny running breathless: "Edward rolled down the hill in a steel culvert; I think he broke his leg!" It may as well have been his leg; for six weeks he wore a cast from heel to thigh to mend one broken toe.

The time we inadvertently left James at the 7-11. An hour later he came running, "Y'forgot me, didn't you!" Owen's picture booklet captioned: "This is my father's friend. I don't know his name but it is nice." The boys rushing in, "Dad, Dad! Were you killed in the war?"

I am the one who wanders and drifts, never belonging, never bonding. I seem to chase a permanence ever eluding me. A game of cat and mouse. A paradox. For if I ever achieve permanence again, it will surely impale me.

Strawberries on Saturday

Dusk descended on South Long Lake like house lights dim-
ming, ground fog resurgent with sorrow hovering over Paradise
Beach. Bowing branches of forest pines swept low over the rising
land, languid as field hands drained of a day's sweat. Beyond
stretched Monty's prized inheritance, the heart gone out of it
now, fields mostly fallow, the barn housing scant replications of
an earlier era, the big house in the grove boarded up after the
folks passed on.

Stooped and deferent to one leg, he hobbled through evening
chores, feeding and watering, bedding the livestock on fresh hay.
Securing the stable for the night, he blew out the lanterns and
started up the stone walkway, pausing on the knoll to pull off his
cap and wipe his face. The setting sun blazed over the strawberry
field below. Another scorcher tomorrow. At this rate the berries
should be ready for picking by Saturday. Headlights came bump-
ing up the section road. Someone dropping in? Nope. Ludwig
Skinner with a load of melons for market tomorrow.

At the door Monty brushed the dirt off his boots and entered
the old bunkhouse, now a make-do cabin for himself. Slinging
his cap onto a hook, he went to the sink and scrubbed to the
elbows. Too hot to cook. He pulled a beer from the refrigerator,
and turning on the radio for the news, sank to the sofa. He rested
his arm on the back, imagining Maybelle beside him smelling like
Lux toilet soap, young legs crossed, red lips ready for his kisses.
Dear, sweet Maybelle. He turned up the volume. Grain prices
down, tract housing swindling young buyers, President Kennedy
heading up the Bay of Pigs fiasco. Waiting for the weather report,
he rested his head and closed his eyes, slipping backward in time,
going over it yet again...

A spring day in 1934...Maybelle came galloping up the driveway on Daybreak, hair wild in the wind. She jumped off and,

hands on hips, shouted, "Monty Jensen! I love you! I love everyone I've ever met! I love everyone I've never met!" She danced
him around in a circle. "What's up?" he laughed.

"Hang on to your hat!" She slapped her thigh, her freckled
face electric. "Next Thursday, next Thursday! I audition for a
scholarship to the Eastman School, in none other than...Roches-
ter, NEW YORK!"

Monty stepped back and sat on the woodpile. The Eastman
School...New York...She spoke a foreign language.

"New York!"

"Ye-e-s!" she squealed. "It's a marvelous opportunity! One of
the best music schools in the country. I looked it up in the library.
Ranks up with Juilliard for Heaven's sake!

He broke the twig in his hand. "Why so far away? What's
wrong with Minnesota?" He swung around. "What about our
plans?"

"Our plans?"

"Our plans to get married and live here...on my land, and...
and raise a family."

"Monty, we're only eighteen years old!"

"What's the point of waiting?" His voice cracked. "I'm ready
Aren't you ready?" He started toward the barn.

She ran to catch up. "Monty! Have you heard nothing I've
said?

"Sounds like a pipe dream to me," he threw over his shoulder,
then stopped and faced her. "I don't see why you'd want to go so
far away and...and ruin everything!" He headed on toward the
barn.

She ran beside him, trying to gauge his will. "Monty, this is
not a pipe dream, it's real! It's now! I'm one of five chosen from
a hundred seventy applicants." Tears filled her eyes. "Please try to
understand...please."

"I do understand! You'll get out yourself out there and forget
all about home. You'll forget all about where you belong. You'll

get all fancy and stuck-up." A whiff of ham drifted from the smoke house. "Aw, come on, Monty! Is that all you're afraid of?" She turned on her heel, mounted Daybreak and was off.

He jammed his hands in his pockets. They'd been pairing off since eighth grade, best friends, meant for marriage and a family right here on the hundred forty acres his grandfather left him; land carved out by generations of Jensens before him. This house where great-grandfather was born a century ago, this is home!

"Montgomery!" His mother was calling him. "Come in and have some lunch. It's after two o'clock!" "Maybelle'll forget her restless ideas in time and learn to be content and raise a family here on the land," he thought. Their duty was here, that was final.

Maybelle headed Daybreak down through the pasture into pine forest. Gone for hours, racing over deer trails, jumping fallen logs, splashing across Boulder Creek, neck open in the wind, later silent and brooding at the dinner table. Where spawned another division. A common midwestern abhorrence of confrontation had frozen an impasse between her parents. Peter measured the secure ground already laid for his daughter if she were to marry into the Jensen line. Hard workers, every one of them. And Monty, he knew who he was. He'd hold to the line.

It was Evelyn, already weathered and leathery keeping her commitment to the land, who saw at an early age the rare gift apparent in her daughter. Scouring the countryside, she'd put her with the best teachers. An inner spark ignited, and Maybelle's drive would not relent. Hours upon hours at the keyboard practicing brought recognition, and dozens of requests to hear the young artist. A performance with the MacPhail Orchestra in Minneapolis won her an audition at the prestigious Eastman School, for which Evelyn was prepared to move heaven and earth that it happen.

Maybelle chose two selections from Eastman's list. She would work five hours a day over eight weeks in preparation for the audition. On Wednesday, April 11th she flew with Evelyn to New York. On Thursday the 12th they sat backstage at Eastman

Performing Arts Building waiting to audition. Maybelle's turn came. She crossed the stage, seated herself at the concert Steinway, brought her hands to the keyboard. Clean lines of poetry traveled the etude down lush gorges, up white peaks, through rich mazes, coming to rest in the end, infinite peace stilling the great hall. Next, rousing assertions of the polonaise firmly in place, the plunge into the restless middle movement, searching, coming nearer and nearer to the final thrilling reunion of themes resounding.

Saturday Maybelle and Evelyn were back home. Two weeks later a letter in the mail. Maybelle flew up Monty's drive on Daybreak. Each of the auditions had been excellent in detail, but Maybelle's impeccable instinct for musical meaning had tipped the scale and won her the scholarship, starting fall semester, 1934. Monty offered Maybelle stilted congratulations, otherwise maintaining a stubborn posture. Frustrated with spurned attempts to communicate with him, she fell into a destructive pattern of needling. Their perfunctory attendance together at summer social functions was only a pretext to placate. Monty was in fact paralyzed with dread of Maybelle's departure for New York.

Until the stacked deck collapsed.

Maybelle finished her five hour session at the piano and started for the stable. She heard the distant rumble of thunder and saw a flash of lightning. Her father called Shep and opened the gate for the cattle. "I wouldn't take time out now, Maybelle. Supper time." "Just a short trot, Dad." She mounted and was off.

She was into the meadow in a flash. Something was wrong. The knoll ahead was spinning. She pulled on the bridle and felt herself sliding. It was the last she remembered. Dinner was getting cold. Peter peered out the window. "She'll be here. You know how she is on that horse. In another world." Suddenly Daybreak galloped through the yard, stopping at the windmill. She reared and whinnied.

They found Maybelle crumpled in a heap in the pasture. At the hospital Dr. Little ran a battery of tests over the next few days, then called a conference with Evelyn. There was a tumor, inoperable, fast growing, already at an advanced stage, unresponsive to the limited options.

The day was in mid-August, trees already tinged here and there with yellow, corn stubbles stiff in the fields. Dark clouds moved rapidly across the rumbling sky, wind whipping, branches snapping. Chickens fluttered toward shelter. Monty ran to tie down a load ready for the hayfork and get the team into the barn. When he emerged Maybelle stood by the windmill, arms and legs bare in the driving rain. He tore off his poncho and ran. "Here, put this on. Goodness! You're soaked!" He caught her hand and pulled her onto the side porch. "I have something to tell you." Apprehension drenched her words. She went on. "You'll be happy to know the good news." "Really! What good news?" Lightning flashed overhead, and a clap of thunder. "What? I can't hear you!" "It's all off," she shouted. "No school! No New York!" Monty caught his breath. "Why…what hap—?" She fired him a brutal look. A bolt of lightning struck, splitting the red oak, smashing the garden gate. "I can't hear you!" he screamed. "I said now we're both chained to this old barn-of-a-house! Stuck in the mud!" Monty cowered in a corner of the swing. "Mud coming out our ears, crusting our hair, caking our fingernails!" Rain ran off the porch in a waterfall. Hail pelted the roof and skipped across the grass, pounding the hollyhocks flat, ripping awnings from the summer kitchen. Maybelle sat, white as marble.

The storm ran its course and the sun came out. The '32 Oldsmobile out front dripped puddles, water slid off leaves, the lawn sparkled with hailstones, Bluebells lay mashed against the windmill. Hens again picked in the yard, the weathervane still spun, steam rose from the strawberry field, plum trees glistened against the blue of a farm sky…a farm sky…a farm sky. She left Monty leaning against the porch column, his head buried in his arms.

She walked home, the road before her young eyes chiseled in granite. That evening a harvest moon sparkled across South

Long Lake. Threshers, tired and sweaty, headed for Paradise
Beach, some on foot, some loaded into Billy Senn's Model A.
They lathered up and dove into the cool water. Monty sat on the
dock, dangling his feet in the water. Maybelle appeared, graceful,
glowing in the dusk like a Rodin masterpiece. She slipped into the
water and moved toward him.

Tears stood in her eyes. She drew his face down and
kissed him hard, then smoothly ascended the diving tower.
He watched her dive, slicing the water. She surfaced, and swam in
strong strokes toward deeper water. "She'll be all right,"
he thought. Nonetheless he shoved a rowboat into the water
and climbed in. In the gathering darkness he lost sight of her.
Grabbing the oars, he quickly turned the boat around and rowed
in her direction. Where was she? "CAN ANYONE SEE
MAYBELLE?"

The splashing crowd failed to hear him. "MAYBELLE!
MAYBELLE!" The crowd, quiet now, formed a drag line.
Clasping hands, they moved back and forth through the water.
Evelyn searched the bath houses. No sign. Someone called the
sheriff. Word spread and neighbors gathered. By 10:00 p.m. men
came with drag hooks and went into deep water, the moonlight
gone now, water black as ink. It was 3:45 a.m. when they raised
her body. Peter collapsed on the beach as his daughter was
carried to the ambulance. Monty and Evelyn rode with her.

The community flocked to the funeral at Long Lake
Community Church. She lay like a waxen bride in lovely white
lace, calla lilies spilling across the casket, her scholarship rolled
in her hand. Daybreak went wild, breaking through the pasture
fence, disappearing in pine forest. He was seen that evening in
the cemetery circling her grave, snorting and rearing. Monty sat
at home, mute, encapsulated in a depth of grief that sealed his
isolation in concrete as cold as Maybelle's tomb, guilt eating the
marrow of his bones. On nights when he could not sleep he
sometimes saw a figure in white wandering the strawberry field
in the moonlight. When he ran toward her she disappeared.

She smiled at him from the shelf. Did you suffer a cramp on that awful night, Maybelle? Were you pulled under, gasping... your lungs filling...Maybelle...Maybelle...Or did you know... did you tell me with your kiss...you would not be back...did you leave me behind, Maybelle...did you...

Peter and Evelyn were gone now, buried beside her in the church graveyard. Young Ludine, too, dead of a stroke at thirty-two. And Gordon Schiller, his arm torn off in a car collision. Billy Senn, just a boy, lost at sea in the war.

The news long over, Monty opened another beer and went in to run a cool tub before bed. Tomorrow he'd weed the strawberries again. Pickers might come by Saturday bright and early, y'never can tell.

A Tragedy on California Street

A slow drizzle hazed the night at San Merced's Crossing. The corner streetlight at Fourth and California Streets barely outlined the ghostly form of Doretta Wagner's house and her '32 Oldsmobile long sunken onto rusted rims under the carport. Rumors of lights on and off, shadows moving across cobwebbed windows, cats yowling, moans from the pumphouse had turned reputation into legend after her death in 1971. A young newspaper reporter from Collier's magazine got wind of the story begging to be told. Arriving in town that day, he stood outside the iron fence, rain dripping from his hat, caught up in the decaying spectre before him, the faded wicker settee on the front porch sagging under the weight of a moss covered roof, paint chips washing away in the downspouts, windows cracked here and there, a garden hose sprawled like a snake across the now junk yard. Vowing to piece together the mystery behind the apparitional neglect, the young man pledged his relentless efforts to uncover the truth.

Months were lengthened into years of research as he dug up evidence, and questioned townspeople reluctant to speak ill of Doretta as though even in death she might exercise vindictive powers over them. The young reporter immersed himself to a point probably beyond wisdom. His story of Doretta, salvaged from the evil wreckage at 1409 California Street, perhaps released her and at last put her to rest. The house was bulldozed to the ground four years after Doretta's death.

The unholy roots shaping the events of Doretta's life began on Summit Avenue overlooking greater St. Paul. Granite and graystone edifices of the day rose from broad lawns bordered in flowering hedges and brick walkways. Massive carriage houses and stables housed handsome teams of horses and their caretakers. Noted surgeon Dr. Charles Wagner and his wife,

Louise, resided in comfort in their fourteen room grey stone mansion on the hill. Six years married and yet childless, they held scarce hope of conceiving a child. The discovery in 1887 that Louise was at last expecting was hailed as miraculous. As her body swelled so did Charles' pride. A son to follow in his footsteps. He would train at Charles' alma mater, Harvard Medical School, in surgery, of course. Father and son known worldwide. Louise listened with quiet indulgence to his dreams for the future life she carried in her womb, wondering indeed how well Charles would cope if his plan slipped to one side or the other with contradictions in the birth, such as a female baby. What then?

He wavered but a moment when the birth of a daughter was announced, as though he had arranged the event with deliberate care. Ah, well. She would be groomed early on for headmistress, or editor, curator perhaps. He must lay a plan starting now.

Louise lay exhausted. Fourteen hours of pushing, panting, and sweating soundly deflated poise and stature. The red slithery creature lay warm on her stomach, its heartbeat pressed to her own, suckling, bonding mother and daughter. Her name would be Doretta, for Charles' late mother.

She was from the start a docile, contented baby, amusing herself at Louise's feet with dolls and noisemakers, making a game of tangling herself in Louise's knitting yarn. Charles disapproved of such play. Doretta's time should be structured to include listening to classical music, learning her letters and numbers, and proper table manners, even though she barely walked or talked.

When Doretta turned three, Charles decided she should ride with him in the carriage on his patient rounds through the cobblestone streets of St. Paul. Louise objected. "Really, Charles, the air has a sharp bite to it. Do you think it's prudent to be exposing Doretta? She's scarcely more than a baby!" "Nonsense! She is a paragon of health! The brisk air will provide hearty stimulation!" Charles countered. Although Louise wrapped Doretta's dark curls snugly in woolen bonnet and shawls, one particularly bleak day Doretta took a chill. In a short time her nose, red and sore, ran, while her temperature rose. Louise put her to bed with hot packs and water bottle, greasing her chest and throat with mentholatum.

The fever raged. Charles put off his other patients in deference to her, and arranged that someone be at her side the clock around. On the sixth day her temperature climbed to 106°F. Charles prepared a tub and gathering her in his arms, immersed her in ice water. Doretta screamed while Charles held her firmly. Finally raising her from the water he wrapped her immediately in a warm blanket and held her. Within the hour the fever broke. Charles collapsed and was led from the room.

Panic at the near fatality gripped Louise. She blamed herself for allowing Doretta out in such weather. She also blamed Charles. As a doctor he should have known better.

Bewildered at Louise's sudden coolness, Charles spent much of his time doing research for an upcoming medical publication. One evening after growing weary of the detailed length the text required, he went out for a stroll. He noticed a group of people waiting in line to see the opera, Aida. On the spur of the moment he found himself joining them outside the opera house.

During intermission he went to the lobby for a smoke. As he held the match to his cigarette, he felt a nudge to his elbow. A tall handsomely dressed woman stood, a cigarette poised in her black velvet glove. Charles held the light for her. Taken aback by her brazen gaze he reddened and returned to his seat in the darkening auditorium.

A short time later Louise's suspicions proved accurate; Charles was finding solace elsewhere. She also discovered she was pregnant. Feeling trapped in the predicament, she sought the services of Dr. Thomas Reedle, who reputedly took care of such situations for a price.

Louise had him summoned to the house. A week later the procedure was all over. Louise lay still in her bed as she was told. Four days later Dr. Reedle hastened to Louise's bedside. The persistent bleeding was out of control. In spite of his best efforts, the infamous Dr. Reedle lost Louise.

Doretta was told her mother had gone away on a trip. For days she watched out the window for the carriage to return. She roamed the house, looking in closets and store rooms, under beds. Their maid, Agnes, in a state of despair, tried to divert her attention with games and favorite treats.

At dinner one evening she was not eating. "What has happened to Mother?" Her father slowly put down his fork. "Mother is not coming back, Doretta." A lump of ice grew in her stomach. "Not ever?" He rose stiffly from the table. "Not ever." He strode away. Doretta jumped down and ran after him. "But Father, where is she? He barely paused. "Where did she go!" He turned an ashen face. "…She left us, baby…she left us…" He swept her up in his arms. They sat in his chair, sobbing together.

Two months later he brought The Woman into the house, introducing her as "your new mother." She stared into Doretta's eyes. "So this is darling Doretta." She swept through the rooms, taking inventory, feeling the satin draperies, snapping her finger against a crystal vase, eyeing a family portrait soon to disappear. Doretta dashed upstairs to the bathroom to be ill.

The lascivious behavior of her father and The Woman toward one another sickened Doretta. She took her family of dolls to the attic, out of sight. Desperate to regain her father's affection, she feigned illness, even catapulted down the long, curved stairway to shock him into examining her. The Woman was not taken in. The following afternoon, as her father drove away, The Woman swung Doretta around and whipped the thongs of her riding crop across the small of her back repeatedly, then pushed her into the cellar and bolted the door.

Doretta clung to the stair rail and slowly descended the steps into the musty smells. As her eyes adjusted to the darkness, the outline of her mother's dress form stood in the silence, her riding saddle slung over a sawhorse. Doretta climbed onto the saddle and laid her cheek against the cold leather. Branches scraped against the basement window, the time interminable until she drifted off to sleep. She awakened with a start to see The Woman staring down at her.

"Doretta! Come upstairs now and practice your piano."
She spoke sweetly, knowing it would put Doretta where Charles best loved to see her. Doretta climbed from the saddle and trudged up the stairs.

"Remember! Not one word…" The Woman's eyes shot fire. Doretta sat at the piano, stumbling through her new scale for the week. The Woman by her side with a hickory switch, quickly rapped her knuckles, "Now then, from the beginning!"

The Woman's beatings and threats continued, while time served to distance her father. Evenings he swilled brandy while mount-ing disagreements with The Woman swelled to violent shouting matches. On Doretta's seventeenth birthday, he fell ill suddenly and died. An autopsy revealed hemlock poisoning.

The Woman put on a credible display of grief, all the while orchestrating an investigation implicating Doretta in the crime. After hours of grueling depositions, the charges were dropped. The Woman then produced a revised will handsomely in her own favor. Devastated at her father's rejection, Doretta took her meager inheritance without protest.

While The Woman went off to New York on a shopping spree, Doretta returned to her once beloved home to pack up her belongings and be gone. Her bags ready at the door, she had yet one sojourn long awaited. She entered the study and began a search through her father's desk. She found keys at the bottom of his stationery drawer, climbed the stairway to a forbidden door, locked since the day of her mother's disappearance. She turned the key and entered the room, breathing her mother's familiar scent. On the dressing table were her mother's photo, young and beautiful, cheek to cheek with baby Doretta; a porcelain rose; and a book about Susan B. Anthony. In the closet she found a purple plumed hat, dresses of velvet, silk, linen; riding boots and crop;

a blue satin bedspread. Where were the pink lace…matched
luggage? She went away without luggage…or clothes?

A newspaper lay folded on the desk, dated March 5, 1893;

WIFE OF PROMINENT SURGEON
BLEEDS TO DEATH

Louise Wagner died of massive hemorrhaging at 3:30 p.m. Tuesday,
March 4, following an abortion performed by Dr. Thomas Reedle.
Household maid, Agnes Flanagan, discovered Mrs. Wagner in her
bed, soaked with blood. Efforts to revive her failed.

The room spun. Doretta sank to the floor. So that was it,
Mother! The Woman already on the scene, you pregnant, Father
such a fool. The fading sunlight washed over the bed where
Mother had slept her last, golden rays sinking into the river below
a closure to the day, to insoluble grief. She rose at last, kissed
the photo and slipped it under her arm, locked the room, and
returned the keys to the study. She rang for a carriage. The clip-
clop of the horses down the drive ended the chapter.

Needing to be far away, Doretta traveled to San Francisco.
Downtown on Sutter Street she entered a small tea room.

All hopes of one day finding her mother were dashed. As the
sun slid out to sea, she drank tea and allowed her heart to empty
and break. The waitress came. "We're closing now, miss."

So am I, thought Doretta. She inquired if there might be a
rooming house nearby. After a minute the waitress said, "There
used to be a hostel for young women over on Acacia Street,
I believe." She watched Doretta gather herself together, noting
her drained face. "Can I be of any help, miss?"

Doretta gave her a wan smile. "I guess you wouldn't know
where to begin."

Outside she caught a trolley to Acacia Street. Once in her
room she fell into bed and slept for twelve hours. She woke to
the sun streaming in the east window. The small desk beneath it
held a bouquet of white daisies, white curtains blowing gently,

a braided rug led to the bath down the hall. She tidied up, put on her clothes and sat down at the desk, trying to assess the events of the last few days. She had no parents, no family save an uncle and a smattering of cousins she barely knew. She had no home. The past was dead. The present was a small rented room, a few clothes, some photos.

A vender called out his wares from the street. She pulled a shawl over her shoulders and stepped outside. The spring air was sharp on her cheeks. Far below the hill, the blue-green ocean moved in swells catching the sun between rumbling white breakers. Far to the left the Golden Gate Bridge was partially obscured by tall buildings. Doretta felt drawn to step onto such a bridge, see where it would lead. A red horse-drawn trolley tripped up the street. In the days and weeks to follow, the repetition of sights and sounds ever in the city evoked the beginning of new responses in Doretta, distancing the austere house, the treachery of The Woman, the evil deaths of both parents, and the dark fears that choked her childhood years.

She found work in a nearby flower shop, and discovered a latent talent for growing plants and arranging bouquets. The soft petals, deep colors, lovely fragrances nursed her bruised senses. One day the shopkeeper, Vera, took her to the University Arboretum at Berkeley, introducing her to exotic genera of which she'd never heard. At Vera's encouragement, Doretta enrolled in horticulture studies at UC Berkeley.

She was assigned a dormitory room and a roommate, rosy faced Mary Beecham, whose devil-may-care outlook proved to be good medicine for Doretta. Mary demanded to know all about Doretta. "Your father?" "Died two months ago." "Oh, how dreadful! Died of what?" Doretta shrugged. "He just died."

Mary scrutinized Doretta's worried countenance, her matronly brown suit, severe boots. She looked as though she hadn't had any fun in a coon's age. "I'm going to have to fix that," she thought. "Tell you what, let's go over to the Union and have a malt. After that I'll show you around campus. "We'll do some boy watching ," she said with a wink. Doretta had never met anyone quite like Mary. She oscillated between bewildered and fascinated in the months to follow.

The temptation to imitate Mary's unabashed responses was hard to resist. Only occasionally did she stumble back into the nightmare barely behind her. She tried to remember that campus life was reality, happening now, that whatever happened in the past was dead.

However, it came back again all too soon. When the time came, Mary asked Doretta where she would be spending fall break, a question for which Doretta was unprepared. "Oh, I have a lot of studying to do. I'll just stay right here." "You can't. The dorms will be closed." Doretta hadn't thought of that. Mary wondered at an eighteen year old girl with no home. "Tell you what, you come home with me. My mom and dad will be delighted. Among my two sisters and brother and me, you'll go virtually unnoticed. Trust me." Doretta reluctantly agreed.

Repressive heat still held the days in Sacramento. Doretta found her San Francisco wardrobe heavy and formal. Mary dragged her off shopping, encouraging flattering pastels. Returning exhausted, the girls sat resting on the front porch swing when the sight of a young man emerging from his carriage in the driveway quite paled Doretta. Standing on the bottom step, he cupped his eyes from the sun, his blonde hair glistening, penetrating Doretta's poise.

Mary jumped the steps, nearly upsetting them both, and threw herself into the young man's waiting arms. They hugged and hugged. "Doretta, meet this old reprobate. He's my brother Edward, I hate to admit." Doretta's eyes rose to meet his, and the proverbial thunderbolt struck.

The week that followed was as near paradise as Doretta could imagine. Mary was her outrageous self, her parents were warm and affectionate, and Edward! Edward was a Greek god by all standards. Witty, attentive, fun, charming, and handsome as she'd ever seen in her life. Before returning to school, Doretta had an invitation to spend Christmas with the Beechams. It couldn't be happening! Old fears glinted through the laughter, ominously hovering overhead. Which world was real?

Doretta was back in the dormitory but a week when a letter from Edward arrived. It invited her to dinner at the Baker Hotel. She happily accepted, knowing that for the next few days her thoughts would be on Edward alone and nothing else.

The following week at dinner, Edward enchanted Doretta with compliments and charming conversation. As they left the dining room, Edward suddenly turned and ascended steps. Doretta's head reeled as he pulled her after him and said, "I have a room here for the night." Before she could respond, Edward unlocked the door to room number 9.

The next morning they sat on a small balcony eating breakfast. He continued whisperings of the night before, his undying devotion, his passionate longing for her. She was a Fairy Princess, smitten, helpless in his hands.

Returning to school, she waited to hear from him. She began to fantasize, longing to crawl onto his lap, be held tightly, be taken with him everywhere he went, never out of his sight.

Doretta wandered around the dorm, floating in a dream, hardly able to concentrate on her studies. Christmas came. She bought lavish gifts for everyone, especially Edward. A gold watch and fob and, curiously, a derby hat. Edward's gift to Doretta was a rhinestone brooch she thought to be diamonds.

Their trysting at the Baker Hotel continued, tea time a routine, like playing house. Pipe and slippers, a glass of brandy, a stroll on the shores, turning down the bed. Doretta slipped into the habit of calling him Daddy, he in turn called her Doll.

After college graduation came the trauma of moving on. Mary took a position in soil conservation in the village of Mendocino, high on a cliff looking forty miles out to sea. Edward, vague about his future, interned at a law firm in Monterey.

Awaiting another tryst, Doretta's fantasy took on a new aggression. Edward would ask for her hand in marriage. She would order a wedding gown from Lord and Taylor in New York, two hundred or maybe three hundred invitations, a reception and dinner at an elegant San Francisco ballroom. They would honeymoon on St. Thomas Island, then make their home in San Francisco where they would overlook the Golden Gate Bridge. She was certain the next time she saw Edward, he would take her as his wife.

She waited for him at the Beecham's home in Sacramento. A longer than healthful interim passed without any word. Mr. Beecham suggested to Doretta that she might try for a position, perhaps teaching or doing clerical work. Doretta's fantasy wavered. A position? Why, Edward would take care of her. Edward, who pledged his undying devotion.

Her funds were running thin. Mr. Beecham, worried about Doretta's mental state, took it upon himself to help her secure a teaching position in a small valley town. The dusty little valley town, dry and dull for a twenty-two year old girl, she traveled to Monterey by train every weekend to be with Edward. He would finish his internship soon and they would be married. He was busy, working hard to win a position with a reputable law firm. He had no time now to spend with her, no time to write her. His ardor would return soon. Very soon.

On June 15th a note from Edward written in his hand on his office stationery arrived. She took it from her box and tore it open. Her face drained.

> *It is with regret I must inform you I can no longer see nor contact you. Pursuant to my marriage to Miss Nettie Lowell, I will be named a full partner in Lowell, Lowell and Beecham. I trust you will understand my position.*
>
> *Ever fondly,*
> *Edward*

Doretta sank to the sofa, reading and re-reading the letter. The doorbell rang several times. She didn't make any effort to answer it. She sat, still as death, long into the evening. Two weeks later an article in the San Francisco Chronicle read:

> *Mr. Beecham's body was found slumped in his chair at Lowell,*
> *Lowell and Beecham, stabbed eleven times. A young woman was seen*
> *rushing from the vicinity and boarding the Bay trolley, after which she*
> *vanished. An investigation revealed Mr. Beecham had been leading a*
> *number of young ladies astray with passionate rhetoric.*

A number of young girls…Doretta staggered about under the consummate rejection. She vowed never again to be vulnerable. Men were cruel liars, cheats. Never to be trusted!

The murder went unsolved.

Doretta retired to her flat, her life over. The dark shadows of her childhood folded over her, suffocating the memories of sun rays over the ocean, frolicking about on campus, the touch, the smell, the secure warmth of Edward. She turned away all callers, refused invitations to the point they were no longer proferred.

Three months later she emerged. Those who saw her were shocked. Gone were the girlish blouses and loose curls.

She stalked down the sidewalk in a stiff black dress, hair pulled into a tight bun, a tote bag and umbrella swinging from her arm, head high in the raw wind. Downtown she entered Mariano's Department Store. As she sauntered down the aisles, her eyes rested on a large pearl-cluster hair clip in the display case. At her request the clerk removed it. It lay before her on the counter. She wanted it. In her life she never wanted anything as much. She asked the clerk to remove several clips from the case. Before a mirror she tried first one, then another. The clerk grew restless and tended another customer. When she returned Doretta murmured that none seemed quite right, thank you. At home she drew the pearl clip from her bag. "Just this once," she thought. "Just this once."

Within a few weeks, however, employees became aware of missing inventory, Mr. Mariano was keeping close watch over his store. When Doretta slipped up one day and appeared wearing a hat he recognized as one from his hat department, he watched her more closely. The hat, a small red felt with a delicate black veil, was stunning against Doretta's dark hair and eyes, a fact not lost on Mr. Mariano, a widower with two young boys to raise. He couldn't bring himself to confront the slender, young beauty he found so attractive.

In January of 1917, Doretta bought a corner lot on California Street from the United Methodist Church, and the building of her house commenced. Much haggling between Doretta and the builder delayed progress. As it was, the timing proved to be bad. Men were one by one being drafted into World War I military service, and carpenters were all but impossible to find. The house dictated by Doretta was never completed, although it was a handsome layout boasting a wide front porch of Victorian filigree. Downstairs pocket doors separated living and dining rooms. There was a central bath, modern for the times. An open stairway led to a second floor. Rooms there were framed in, rafters open to the roof, floors rough boards. Holes were drilled for bathroom fixtures which were never installed. Finished or not, lights and activity went on up there. Some thought Doretta was accumulating loot brought in at night from who knows where. Did she have a market for the goods she stole? No one knew from where her livelihood came, let alone the funds to build the house.

One year later a young man said to be Doretta's nephew came to live with her, Did no one know she was an only child? Her countenance mellowed. She wore dresses revealing slender ankles, hair cropped in a daring bob. She returned to teaching, took an active part in local politics, and started an adult literacy program. One progressive citizen of Merced wrote a story about Doretta, which was published in Collier's. The senior editor of the magazine, attracted by the lovely photo of Doretta, made it his business to meet the young woman in person.

He contacted her and persuaded her to have dinner with him. She chose a stunning red dress, a clustered pearl clip fastened in her hair. She stood before the mirror straightening the seams of her stockings, then sat on the edge of the bed. She was uneasy and had a bad feeling about the man.

What kind of interrogation would he put her through? Would he be fat? Bald? Fresh? Or tall and skinny with thick glasses? A long crooked nose? Up to no good?

The doorbell rang. She froze. It rang again. And again. She dared not move. He pressed the buzzer and held it. Doretta crept to the bedroom door and locked it. Finally the ringing stopped and she heard his carriage pull away. When the nephew came home an hour later, unsteady on his feet, speech slurred, he inquired why she was all "dolled up." "Go to bed! You're a sight!" she snapped.

It was rumored the nephew was seen at the County Fair with a young Merced girl. On a hot summer's night, an unsettling quarrel thundered from Doretta's house. Mr. Mariano gave the nephew an ultimatum, after which the nephew disappeared and was not seen again. Doretta drew her blinds and barricaded the doors with stacks of newspapers and magazines.

Carpenters came and enclosed the front porch, installing triple locks. She came and went through a side door mostly hidden by an overgrown hedge.

Soon after that, in 1925, Doretta received notice from her father's attorney that The Woman had died, bequeathing the small remainder of the estate she'd squandered on opulent living to her grandniece. An irrevocable will dated May, 1887, naming Doretta the sole heir upon the death of the last surviving parent surfaced among her father's papers. Did Doretta wish to contest the latest disposition, fraudulent in view of the previous assignment? The mere thought dredged up anew the grief surrounding her father's death. Yes, she wished to contest! Her growing outrage rekindled an appetite to do in these impostors this time, once and for all. The nasty battle waged in court exhibited stealth and greed at their extreme, and though Doretta prevailed, she went away embittered, suspicious of judicial processes, convinced that great manipulative maneuvers were the business of the day for the most trivial of transactions, and motives behind them suspect in every case.

In August of 1932 she re-invented her station with a stately new Oldsmobile. The car shot from her driveway, let oncoming motorists beware. Fierce eyes through the windshield warned the boldest to stay out of her path. Downtown she parked where she pleased, scorning citations she took home and threw in the pumphouse. "Doretta, you can't park by a fire hydrant." "Can't? *Can't?*" Move on or I'll have you arrested!" By arrangement with Mr. Mariano, patrol officers shook their heads and let her go.

Eight years passed. She no longer mowed nor watered. Weeds choked through withered lilacs, cracking the foundation of her house. Paint peeled from the weathered siding. Two more additions were built, insulating and darkening the living and dining rooms, their windows facing into the adjuncts.

Doretta's deteriorating behavior alarmed her neighbors. She frothed and bullied at every turn, disrupting city council meetings, railing over cracks in her sidewalk, refusing to pay taxes, balking at funding for city improvements.

Then came 1941, Pearl Harbor, and the nation at war. A system of rationing was to be set in place, she heard. She promptly stocked her pumphouse with cans of gasoline and tires; her cellar with sugar, silk stockings and cigarettes, though it was a pipe she smoked, it was said.

People came and went at odd hours, carrying bags of every size. Was a black market operating on California Street? She loaded her shelves and lined her purse, which now held a gun. No one ventured to play hero and turn her in.

In years following the war she was seen in public less and less. Groceries and other supplies appeared regularly on her back doorstep, delivered daily, mostly by Mr. Mariano himself.

One day she heard him in the driveway. "Mr. Mariano!" "Doretta! I was…I just happened by." "Mr. Mariano! So it's been you…" Overcome, she reached up; her arms went around his neck. He gathered her in his arms, believing that he could finally take a proper place in her life.

He bent to kiss her. She suddenly bolted and stumbled backward. "No, no. It's too late for us, Mr. Mariano. Look at us, our hair gray already. We'd be the laughing stock!" He knew he'd frightened her. "What do we care, Doretta? I've loved you all these years. Years wasted." "I'm so confused…" He reached for her again, and again she backed away. "Tomorrow. We'll talk tomorrow." She turned away and closed the door. "All right. Tomorrow." He slowly drove home. The following day the shades were drawn and the doors locked.

In years following the war, Doretta brought her cousin, Ellen, to live with her. Neighbors were relieved. Now poor aging Doretta would have companionship in her declining days. They were Ellen's declining days, as it happened. Doretta did her best, relying on old-wives' remedies. Nonetheless Ellen's health worsened. On an August day Doretta called a mortician to remove Ellen's body. The persistent odor forever in her bedroom would belie the story Ellen had died in her sleep the night before.

Toward the end, well-wishers looking in on Doretta found fresh flowers daily. Then knocks on her door were followed by silence. On April 10th, 1971, Mr. Mariano, bearing fresh flowers and clean laundry, found Doretta near death. Within the hour she died in his arms. St. Bridgette's Gazette gave this report:

…Doretta never married, although letters from a suitor were found in the pumphouse. A number of dresses, jewelry and other items still bearing price tags were taken from her home after her death. Newspapers and magazines dating as early as 1934 were stacked to the ceilings, forming narrow corridors wending through the eight rooms on the first floor. Doretta willed her assets, totaling $235,000, to the United Methodist Church.

A man claiming to be her nephew appeared in town following her death. He contested Doretta's will, charging the church vestry with coercing Doretta at a time she was no longer of sound mind. The nephew failed to prove he was a nephew…

The story of Doretta haunted the young reporter from Collier's far into his own tormented life. Married and divorced twice, he lost his employment in 1991, unable to bring in fresh stories. He frequently slipped into a desultory preoccupation with a tragic turn-of-the-century maiden for whom, he lamented, he was born too late. He died of alcoholism at the age of forty-nine.

Vivian Senn Liners

June 14, 1931 – April 15, 2006

A native Minnesotan, Vivian Senn Liners was teaching piano
and directing choirs by the age of sixteen. She taught in
Brainerd, Minnesota at the Geisler School, continuing at Kullberg
Piano Studios in Wayzata, Minnesota. She was named choral
director and choreographer of Children's Theatre in Minneapolis.
She directed church choirs and/or served as organist for
community choruses in Pequot Lakes, Brainerd, Minneapolis,
and Worthington, Minnesota; Los Banos, California; and
Fairbanks, Alaska. She is a past member of the Minnesota League
of Poets and the National Federation of State Poetry Societies,
and winner of numerous poetry awards. While working in the
Tutorial Center at Hartnell College, she earned academic credits
for authoring a novel, *Caramels and Callouses.* She later wrote five
books of poetry, essays and short pieces, is mother of four and
grandmother of six, and lived with her husband, Henry, on Upper
Whitefish Lake, Minnesota.